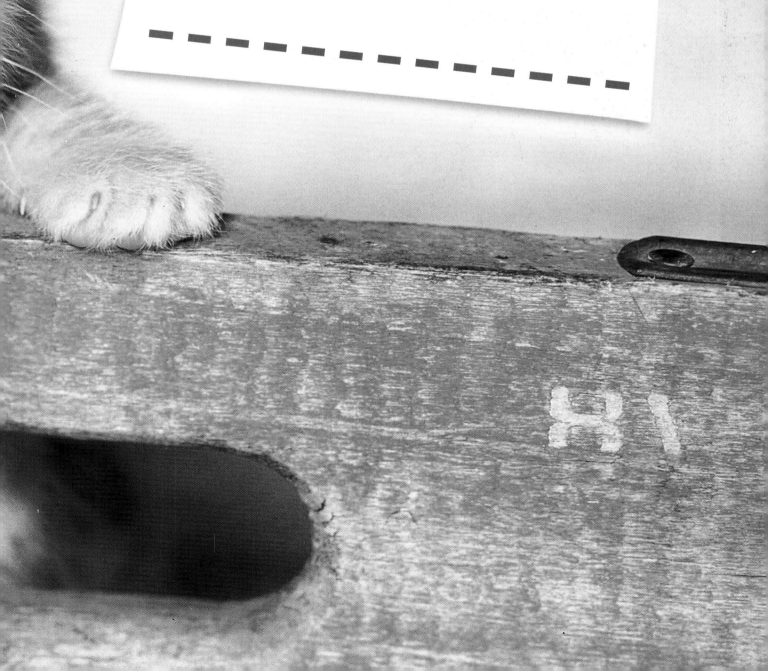

 This **Girl TALK** Annual 2003 belongs to:

_ _ _ _ _ _ _ _ _ _ _ _

Girl TALK

Hello!

Welcome to another fun-packed Girl Talk annual! Inside you'll find great fashion features, a pop quiz and super sleepover suggestions. There are also features showing you how to write your own TV script and draw your own strip cartoon. Plus, there are stories, puzzles and things to make. Why not join in the fun and games? There's so much to do!

Cover girl

Name Emma
Age 12
Hobbies horse riding and swimming
Favourite famous person Britney Spears
Ambition to become a solicitor

girltalk.magazine@bbc.co.uk

First published in 2002 by BBC Worldwide Limited Woodlands, 80 Wood Lane, London W12 0TT
Text, design and illustrations © BBC Worldwide Limited 2002

Make Its devised by Nathalie Abadzis
Studio photography by John Englefield
With thanks to Lauren

pp 6, 7, 8, 9 Sweet Valley Kids concept © Francine Pascal. All rights reserved.
Photographs: David Watts
Script: Carol Warwick

Photographs: Bruce Coleman - pp 2, 3. John Green - pp 46, 47.

Text: Rachel Bell - pp 10, 11, 26, 27. Moira Butterfield - pp 24, 25, 31, 56, 57. Sarah Jacobs - pp 14, 15, 16, 17. Liz MacDonald - pp 54. Heather Maisner - pp 38, 39. Ruby Mather - pp 50, 51. Emma Milne - pp 34, 35. Davey Moore - pp 44, 45. Alison Viña - pp 20, 21, 22, 23.

Illustrations: Emily Bannister - pp 28, 29, 50, 51. Paul Cemmick - pp 14, 15, 16, 17. Simon Clare - pp 36, 37. Mattie Grimshaw - pp 24, 31, 32, 33, 44, 45. David le Jars - pp 25. Dom Mansell - pp 34, 35. Andy Peters - pp 42, 43. Jan Smith - pp 38, 39, 56, 57.

Printed and bound in Belgium

ISBN 0 563 532,36 X

INSIDE

I thought you two might appreciate some cold drinks.

Thanks, Mum. Look, Torn Jeans are appearing at Sweet Valley Theatre tonight.

They've added a special one-off concert date to the end of their tour.

Are they famous?

Mum! They were on *Top of the Pops* last week.

The line's constantly engaged. I can't get through.

We'll have to go down there.

I can't take you now, I've got things to do.

Please, Mum. Please…

We want to be as near the front as possible.

Yes, right below the stage.

I'm afraid you're going to be disappointed, girls.

Torn Jeans sold out Tonight only

Oooooohh no!

Continued over page

7

You can listen to our Torn Jeans CD with us if you want.

...mum ...he front ...s ringing ...ges.

No point, I'm going to see them live tonight.

How did you manage to get a ticket? They were sold out when we arrived.

My dad knows the manager of the Sweet Valley Theatre.

You heard. For five hours this afternoon, both of you must do exactly what I say.

Nothing is worth that!

Well, it's up to you. It seems to me it's not much to ask for the tickets.

And Elizabeth can tidy up my room for me.

Easy.

I think I spoke too soon.

Off you go, then. I'm going to watch TV.

Can the twins last the full five hours? Find out on page 58.

Girl TALK

POP QUIZ

ARE YOU UP TO DATE WITH THE LATEST POP CHARTS? TRY THIS QUIZ TO FIND OUT JUST HOW MUCH YOU KNOW!

1 It looks like this lady is getting in a twist. Do you know what her name is?

2 Who sang *It's OK*?
a. Britney
b. Atomic Kitten
c. Kylie

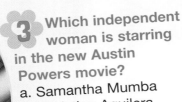

3 Which independent woman is starring in the new Austin Powers movie?
a. Samantha Mumba
b. Christina Aguilera
c. Beyoncé Knowles

4 Posh posed with a panther, but what pet pal did Britney carry around her neck for a performance?
a. A squirrel
b. A python
c. A kitten

5 About 10,000 kids from around the UK auditioned to be in S Club Juniors. How many made it into the band?
a. Eight
b. Nine
c. Ten

6 Can you match these singers to the right song titles?

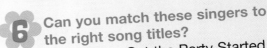

Victoria Beckham   Get the Party Started
Pink   A Mind Of Its Own
Christina Milian   Calling
Geri Halliwell   AM to PM

7 And what's the name of Britter's movie?

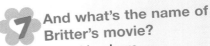

a. Road to Nowhere
b. Highway to Heaven
c. Crossroads

8 Which ex-Neighbours star sings *Kiss Kiss*?
a. Natalie Imbruglia
b. Kylie
c. Holly Vallance

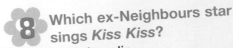

12 When Kym Marsh left Hear'Say, which band member was she rumoured to have fallen out with?
a. Noel
b. Myleene
c. Suzanne

9 Which teen queen signed her first record contract at the age of 12?
a. Jessica Simpson
b. Mandy Moore
c. Kaci

13 Which Pop Idol judge became famous for being mean and nasty?
a. Simon Cowell
b. Pete Waterman
c. Doctor Fox

10 A*Teens sang *Heartbreak Lullaby* on the soundtrack for a hit movie. But which one?
a. The Princess Diaries
b. Monsters Inc.
c. Boys and Girls

14 What's the name of the Australian Hear'Say?
a. Bardot
b. Sydney
c. Lemony

11 So you think you know your girlbands? Name the groups these singing sistas belong to?
a. Jenny, Liz and Tash
b. Alesha, Sabrina and Su-Elise
c. Beyoncé, Kelly and Michelle

15 Which of these singers has her own fashion label?
a. Gabrielle
b. J-Lo
c. Louise

11

WORLD OF

Hot Hit Cover

Use this space to design a CD cover of your own. Choose your favourite band or singer, then cut out and stick pictures of them on the cover, and decorate with glitter or whatever you think will look groovy!

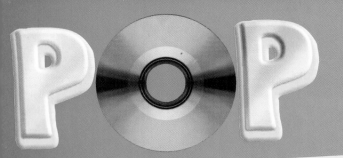

POP

If you're a popoholic, then here's a chance to design your very own CD cover and make a cool CD box to carry all your favourite tunes in.

Make a CD Box

Put your favourite CDs in this box and keep it near the music system. You could make one to keep in the car, too.

What you'll need:
- Three or four cereal boxes
- Ruler and pencil
- Scissors
- Coloured card
- Glue and sticky tape
- Coloured paper or photos to decorate your box

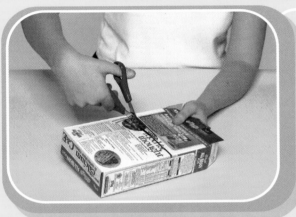

1 Measure 13 cm up from the bottom of each cereal box. Mark the measurement around the box and draw a line between the marks. Cut round the line.

2 To make section dividers, cut three or four pieces of coloured card to the size of the boxes, with five centimetres extra at the top to write the section names on. Glue one divider to the back of each box. Now glue the boxes together. When dry, tape all round it to make it sturdy.

3 Decorate your CD box with pieces of coloured paper or photos of your favourite bands.

4 Write the CD titles on the cards between each section.

Girl BAND

1) IT'S HALF TERM AND THE GIRLS ARE AT A LOOSE END...

I WISH THE SUN WOULD COME OUT. I HATE BEING STUCK INSIDE.

I'M SO BORED AND MY DRUMSTICKS ARE BROKEN.

WE NEED A PLAN.

2) LISTEN UP! IT SAYS HERE ON THE WEBSITE THAT JANGLES THEME PARK IS OPENING A NEW RIDE TODAY. WHY DON'T WE ASK IF WE CAN GO?

COOL IDEA! I BET MY MUM WILL TAKE US.

3) OOH, THE NEW ROLLERCOASTER LOOKS REALLY SCARY.

JANGLES amusement park

YEAH, BUT IT'S TECHNOLOGY-TASTIC!

HEY! WHAT'S THAT FUNKY SOUND?

A JAZZ BAND! THEY SURE CAN PLAY.

4) LOOK, THERE ARE SOME SPARE INSTRUMENTS OVER THERE. LET'S ASK IF WE CAN JOIN IN.

5) HOORAY!!!

THANKS, GIRLS! THAT WAS BRILLIANT. WE HAVEN'T PLAYED LIKE THAT SINCE THE DAYS WHEN WE WERE FAMOUS. WHAT I'D GIVE TO BE ON THE ROAD AGAIN...

6) NEW RIDE opening today!

COME ON, YOU LOT. ENOUGH DAWDLING. MY FAVOURITE SINGER, GLORIA JOLLY, IS OPENING THAT NEW RIDE.

WOW! A REAL STAR. I'M GOING TO ASK HER FOR TIPS ON BEING FAMOUS.

CLUED UP

ACROSS

2 To snatch something fiercely (4)
5 A golden ball of fire in the sky (3)
7 A huge body of water (5)
9 If you agree, you say _ _ _ (3)
10 This can be full or crescent (4)
11 As well (3)
13 The milkman delivers a _ _ _ _ of milk (4)
15 You must _ _ _ _ _ on the door if you want to come in (5)
17 Do you help to _ _ _ the table for dinner? (3)
19 You will find your _ _ _ bone below your waist (3)
20 George is the patron _ _ _ _ _ of England (5)
21 This colour can mean danger (3)
22 What an artist balances the canvas on (5)
25 This planet looks as if it has rings around it (6)
27 If you have an _ _ _ _, you might scratch it (4)
29 A big cat with lots of spots (7)
30 A red jewel (4)

DOWN

1 To poke your nose into other people's business (3)
2 A blast of wind (4)
3 You shout this to make someone jump (3)
4 A female bird often found on a farm (3)
5 Possibly the slowest creature in the world! (5)
6 Eddie Murphy is The _ _ _ _ _ Professor (5)
8 Don't be late for your school trip or you'll miss the _ _ _ _ _ (5)
10 The Loch Ness _ _ _ _ _ _ _ is supposed to live in a loch in Scotland (7)
12 Two letters used to show you agree (2)
14 Everyone has a first _ _ _ _ and a surname (4)
16 You need lots of wind if you want to fly this (4)
18 Traditional clothing worn by Scotsmen (4)
20 Your aunt may be your mum's _ _ _ _ _ _ (6)
23 If you aggravate someone, you _ _ _ _ _ them (5)
24 Someone who never tells the truth (4)
26 The opposite of beautiful (4)
28 A group of cows (4)

18

BRITNEY
MADONNA
GABRIELLE
PINK
GERI
HALLIWELL
KYLIE
MINOGUE
ALLSTARS
KACI
DESTINY'S
CHILD
ATOMIC
KITTEN
SAMANTHA
MUMBA
LOUISE
S CLUB
JUNIORS

```
Z K Y L I E M I N O G U E N F
E A I N I H X Q S E S F L T D
L B G C E Y E H D R S A J E W
L M L E A T O E A H L I S Z S
E U I J R K T T M M X T U R N
I M B P O I S I K A I O O O S
R A E M M L H K K N D I B V L
B H R Z L S S A Y C N O T O R
A T T A F B D ' L U I G N R M
G N Y B R M S L J L U M C N U
K A V B V C S B N J I B O D A
H M N U H R U L G X Q W G T I
R A L I J L S B R I T N E Y A
T S L C C U A T X D C I W L W
U D Y S S X M R J K K N I P L
```

PLUS ONE

EACH WORD CAN BE CHANGED INTO A DIFFERENT WORD BY ADDING ONE LETTER. USE THE CLUES TO WORK OUT THE NEW WORDS.

1	SHOT	Not very tall	....
2	OLD	A yellow precious metal	....
3	SOLD	Something that is very firm	....
4	BEAK	To snap something	....
5	SEAL	To take what isn't yours	....
6	HUG	Something massive	....
7	WARM	A lot of bees	....
8	BUY	What a dog does to a bone	....
9	SELF	Put books on this	....

ANSWERS: 1 SHORT, 2 GOLD, 3 SOLID, 4 BREAK, 5 STEAL, 6 HUGE, 7 SWARM, 8 BURY, 9 SHELF.

19

Becky and the Bridesmaid's Blues

A Story By Alison Viña

The stone was the most beautiful thing I had ever seen. It glistened and sparkled and shone. And it was the most gorgeous colour – my favourite colour – deep, dark red.

Me and Mum had gone to buy a special present for my Auntie Ruby who lives in Australia. She was coming to England to get married.

I'd never met my Auntie before, except once when I was a baby, and I don't remember that. So I didn't know what kinds of things she liked. But I was sure anyone would like this. It was a necklace. It had a long gold chain, with an oval-shaped pendant. And in the middle of the pendant was the stone – a ruby.

"A ruby for Ruby," smiled Mum holding up the necklace. "We'll take it," she said to the jeweller. He put it in a special red box and into a bag, and handed it to Mum.

My mum is a florist and sometimes I help her in the shop. Mum likes all the little delicate flowers like pansies and daisies, and those tiny white flowers called gypsyfeelers or something. Not me. My favourite flowers are red roses. Their velvety petals are really pretty. But I think there's something dark and mysterious about them, too. They look beautiful but can be bad-tempered as well. I've been pricked by their thorns more times than I can remember.

I was helping Mum out one Saturday when she told me about Auntie Ruby's wedding.

"I got some wonderful news today, Becky," she said as she poured us both a cup of tea. "Your Auntie Ruby sent me an e-mail to say she's getting married."

"Fantastic!" I said, feeling excited. "Does that mean we get to go to Australia?"

"I'm afraid not," chuckled Mum. "She wants to get married in England so that all the family can come."

"And there's more," Mum smiled and put her arm around me. "She wants you to be her bridesmaid."

I nearly choked on my tea. You probably think that most girls would be head over heels about being a bridesmaid, don't you? Not me. I couldn't think of anything worse.

Well, it's not that I didn't like the idea of feeling important for a day. The thing I was really worried about was the dress. At least, not the dress itself, more the colour of the dress. Pink. Horrible, pale pink. Pretty, dull, pointless pink. A frilly pink dress. Yuck. I couldn't think of anything worse. You see, I really love red but I really, really hate pink.

Of course, I didn't want to seem ungrateful. So I said how thrilled I was. But as the days passed I began to feel more and more nervous.

Auntie Ruby is really good at dressmaking and Mum said she would be making her own dress and mine.

I had to stand on a chair while Mum took loads of measurements.

"Mum," I said nervously as she put a tape measure round my waist. "H-h-h-has Ruby decided what colour my dress will be?"

"Not yet," said Mum. "I think she's still looking at samples."

But a couple of weeks later my worst fears were confirmed. Mum had asked me to find her address book. She always kept it on a table in the hall. I picked it up and underneath was a magazine called 'Beautiful Brides'. It was open at a section on bridesmaids. And, of course, they were all wearing pink. I didn't say anything to Mum. I would only have to wear the dress for one day after all. I'd just have to grin and bear it.

A few days later I heard Mum talking to my aunt on the phone. "The samples you sent are great," she said, as she took some pieces of pink fabric out of an envelope.

That evening Mum made my favourite dinner – pizza and chips. But I wasn't hungry. I felt horrible and selfish, but I couldn't stop thinking about the dress.

"What's wrong, love?" asked Mum.

"Nothing," I lied. "I guess I'm just nervous about the wedding."

"Well, we've got the cakes to make tomorrow," said Mum. "That'll take your mind off your nerves."

The next day I helped measure out all the ingredients – raisins, currants, sultanas, flour, eggs, sugar.

Flower Power

21

And we mixed everything up in an enormous bowl.

"You know, it's hard to believe that my little sister is getting married," sighed Mum. "She'll look so beautiful in a wedding dress and with that ruby necklace."

I had forgotten about the necklace. "Can I see it again, Mum?" I asked.

"Of course," she said. "It's in the top drawer of the dresser."

I found the necklace and gazed at the stone's wonderful dark beauty. "It's so lovely," I sighed. "I can't wait to see Ruby's face when we give it to her."

The day finally came for Ruby to arrive. Mum picked up her and her fiancé, Mark, from the airport.

I was excited about meeting my aunt and I helped Dad make a special dinner. A proper English roast beef dinner with Yorkshire puddings and roast potatoes. Yum yum!

"Ooh, that smells scrummy," said Ruby as she walked in. "And you must be Becky," she said, as she gave me a big hug.

Ruby was nothing like I thought she'd be. She looked a bit like my mum only younger. But my mum always wears colours like grey and black. And her hair's always short and tidy.

Ruby's hair was long and curly and kind of wild. And she was wearing really cool trousers and a top in different shades of red.

We ate our roast beef and Ruby and Mark told us loads of funny stories about Australia. Then Ruby said, "It's time you saw your dress, Becky. You're going to love it."

I suddenly felt really nervous. I wasn't going to love it at all and I wasn't very good at pretending. The dress was in one of those special zip-up travel bags.

"Now, I know all girls like pink…" said Auntie Ruby, as she started to unzip the bag. My heart sank.

"…apart from you." Auntie Ruby smiled as she held up the most amazing deep red silk bridesmaid's dress.

I couldn't believe it. It was the most fabulous dress I had ever seen. And the colour was perfect.

"Do you like it?" asked Ruby.

"Like it?" I was positively bursting with

excitement. "It's brilliant. I mean, I love it!"

"I'm not called Ruby for nothing, you know," smiled my aunt. "Your mum told me about how you love red. Well, I'm nuts about red, too. I guess it runs in the family."

Then I remembered the necklace. "Then you'll love the special present we bought you," I said jumping up with excitement. "Mum, can we give it to Auntie Ruby now, please?" I pleaded.

"Okay, okay, Becky," Mum laughed. "You know where it is." I rushed to the dresser.

"It's to wear on your special day," I said, handing the box to Auntie Ruby. But as Auntie Ruby opened the box, I had the shock of my life. There was the gold necklace with the

back the tears. "It would have looked brilliant on you."

Ruby gave me a hug. "Well, there's no time to be sad, there's still lots to do," she said.

The next day was the day before the wedding and I helped Mum with all the last-minute preparations. I helped with the flowers – dark red roses, bright red tulips and soft red carnations. Then I blew up loads of red balloons. I started to forget about the necklace and look forward to the wedding.

The wedding was brilliant. I felt like a princess in my dress and Ruby looked cool. She wore a cream silk dress with a pink trim. That was what the sample of pink fabric was for. It actually looked pretty good on Ruby. I took plates of food round to all the guests. And we had our picture taken a million times. I still felt a bit sad about the necklace though. I really wanted to give Auntie Ruby her ruby.

"You've been the perfect bridesmaid, Becky," Auntie Ruby said as she handed me a piece of cake.

I was just about to eat my cake when I noticed a little piece of shiny red cherry in amongst the raisins and sultanas. Then I remembered we hadn't put any cherries in the cake. I took a closer look and realized what it was. The ruby! It must have fallen in the day we made the cake. I jumped up and down with excitement.

Mum laughed, "We'll clean it up and get the jeweller to put it back in the necklace."

"It's beautiful," said Ruby with tears in her eyes. I felt so happy I could cry, too. But, I decided to eat my cake instead. And it was scrummy.

oval-shaped pendant. But, instead of a ruby, there was just a dent in the metal. The stone had gone.

"Oh, no!" said Mum, when she saw it. "The stone must have fallen out. Oh, Ruby, I'm so sorry."

"No worries," said Auntie Ruby. "Come on, let's look for it."

We searched high and low, turning the house upside down. I looked under tables, in drawers, on the floor, in the washing machine, everywhere. But the ruby was nowhere to be found.

"It was a lovely thought," said Ruby at last. "But I've got other necklaces."

"But it was so pretty," I choked, holding

The End

Sleepover Invitations

Make these FUNKY INVITATION CARDS to invite your friends to your sleepover party.

1 Cut a sheet of A4 paper so it is twice the size of the envelope. Fold the sheet in half to make a card. Then flatten it again.

2 Trace round the flower template at the bottom of the page. Transfer the tracing to the second sheet of A4 paper and cut around the outline. Colour the flower brightly.

3 Fold the flower down the middle with the coloured side upwards. Then flatten the flower again and fold the tabs underneath it. Put a spot of glue on the underside of each tab.

4 Lay the flower flat inside the card with the tabs folded underneath it. The middle fold of the flower should run down the middle of the card. Press on the tabs to make them stick.

5 When you open your invitation the flower will pop up! Write your sleepover details on the front of the invitation and around the flower.

24

HONEY POPCORN

Remember when you're popping corn, don't take the lid off the saucepan or you'll have a lot of clearing up to do.

INGREDIENTS TO MAKE ONE BOWL

50 g (2 oz) butter
Two tablespoons of popcorn kernels
Three tablespoons of clear honey

1 Put three-quarters of the butter into a large saucepan that has a lid. Melt the butter over a low heat. Then sprinkle the popcorn in and put the lid on.

2 Cook on a moderate heat, shaking the pan every now and again until there are definitely no more popping noises.

3 Put the rest of the butter in a frying pan and melt it gently with the honey. Stir the mixture into the popcorn. Turn the popcorn out onto a greased baking sheet and leave it to cool down.

SPICY NUTS

Serve these cold in a bowl. They'll disappear really quickly! Leave out the Tabasco if you want a milder version.

INGREDIENTS

One tablespoon of cooking oil
One tablespoon of soy sauce
One beaten egg white
A dash of Tabasco sauce
110 g (4 oz) of shelled almonds or Mixed shelled nuts

1 Put the oven on to 140°C (275°F, gas mark 1).

2 Mix everything together in a bowl and spread the nuts on a baking sheet. Cook in the oven for six minutes, then take the tray out and stir the nuts round. Cook them for another six minutes.

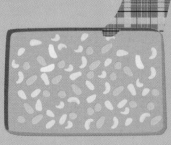

3 Take the tray out of the oven. Leave to cool, and enjoy sharing them with your friends!

start

1

Who presents The Official UK Top 40?
a. Ant and Dec
b. Joe and Dani
c. Connie and Adrian

2

3

4

34

CHALLENGE
Tell a joke that gets some giggles.

32

33

Can you name the four houses in 'Harry Potter and the Philosopher's Stone'?

30

FUN STOP!
Give another player a funky new hair style using plaits and four bobbles.

31

51

53

Who was the female presenter of the Brit Awards 2002?
a. Cat Deeley
b. Zoe Ball
c. Margherita Taylor

52

Name three action heroines from TV or the movies.

54

Name all the Powerpuff Girls to fly ahead two spaces.

29

50

Which pop singer has made a movie in the US called 'Time Machine'?
a. Samantha Mumba
b. Emma Bunton
c. Alicia Keys

FUN STOP!
Find a hairbrush and some sunglasses and do your best impersonation of Britney!

28

PARTY TIME GAME

27

CHALLENGE
You've forgotten your animal slippers. Do not move on until you roll a six to join the gang again.

49

48

Which actor is weaving webs as superhero Spiderman?
a. Tobey Maguire
b. Elijah Wood
c. Josh Hartnett

47

46

Name three fruits beginning with the letter P.

26

25

CHALLENGE
Go and find a scrunchie hair band.

24

23

Name four cats that live in the wild.

22

CHALLE
Sing ou ten ice flav

Name the town where Dawson's Creek is set.
a. Riverside
b. Capeside
c. Lakeside

FUN STOP!
You've got five minutes to give another player a pink makeover using pink make-up and something pink to wear!
6

7

What's the name of Sabrina's furry friend?
a. Smokey
b. Fluffy
c. Salem
8

CHALLENGE
Draw a picture of a cowgirl to ride ahead two spaces.
9

38

10

Who's the little girl who causes big trouble in Monsters Inc.?
a. Bee
b. Lou
c. Boo
37

35

36

What groovy toon has been made into a live-action movie starring Sarah Michelle Gellar?
a. The Simpsons
b. Scooby Doo
c. Recess
39

FUN STOP!
Ask the player to your right what song she'd like to hear, then blast it out on the CD player!
11

55

Who is the author of the book, 'Sleepover'?
a. Jacqueline Wilson
b. Ann M Martin
c. JK Rowling
56

CHALLENGE
Sing the chorus to an S Club song.
56

finish

40

12

What does SMS stand for on a mobile phone?
a. Smiley Man Signal
b. Short Message Service
c. See Me Soon
13

Play this board game with your friends and see who can answer the questions correctly and get to the end first. You will need a dice. Try using small, different-coloured sweets as counters (but make sure they don't get eaten as you play!). You might want to appoint a game master to check your answers on page 62. If you get an answer wrong you miss a turn.

Which American drama is all about Superman growing up?
a. Smallville
b. Enterprise
c. Popular
41

Name five fashion items to get the gypsy girl look.
14

UN STOP!
o-ray! Make a ummy sleepover ack with something yellow in it for everyone.

44

What word do the Americans use for 'school term'?
a. Fall
b. Recess
c. Semester
43

CHALLENGE
Sing the theme tune to Neighbours as if it were an R 'n' B tune!
42

15

20

FUN STOP!
Do any part of a Kylie dance routine.
19

18

Name three films with an animal in the title.

17

What colour blazer do the pupils of Grange Hill have to wear?
a. Purple
b. Black
c. Blue
16

21

27

ARE YOU A GOOD BEST FRIEND?

Are you always there for your chum, or do you run off when she needs you most? Do our quiz and add up your score to see!

1 Your friend and her mum invite you round to try the cakes they've just baked. They're not very nice. What do you do?

a) Pull a face and tell them that the cakes make you feel sick.

b) Have a nibble and politely say that you're really full up.

c) Munch the whole cake and say that it was really delicious!

2 Your best friend has just had her hair cut short. It doesn't really suit her. What do you say?

a) "Ha ha! It makes you look daft – just like..."

b) "It's a bit short. But don't worry, it will grow back soon."

c) "It looks very nice! And short hair is really trendy!"

3 Your friend gets a really cute new puppy, just like the one you've always wanted. What do you do?

a) Tell her that you really don't like puppies.

b) Call your friend a copy cat because you had wanted one first!

c) Offer to help look after the puppy.

4 Your friend tells you a really juicy secret about herself, which you've promised not to tell anyone else. What do you do?

a) Tell everyone you know.

b) Tell one other friend. It's far too juicy for you to keep it entirely to yourself.

c) Keep the secret. That's what friends are for.

5 You're going to a birthday party with your friend. She comes to meet you at your house, but she's wearing the same dress as you. What do you do?
a) Cry and refuse to go unless your friend changes her dress.
b) Decide not to change, but then sulk at the party.
c) Have a good laugh about it and change into another dress.

6 You and your friend sit the same history exam. She gets a higher mark than you. Do you:
a) Say she was really lucky.
b) Say it was an easy exam but you hadn't revised enough.
c) Congratulate her.

7 Your friend tells you she's going on a pony-trekking holiday. You've always wanted to do this but you aren't allowed to. Do you:
a) Sulk and say you hope it rains.
b) Say that ponies are smelly but ask for a souvenir anyway.
c) Tell your friend to have a really good time and suggest you try to go on holiday together next time.

8 Your friend has recently learnt to knit and she has decided to knit you a scarf. Her knitting is so bad the scarf has holes in it. Do you:
a) Hide the scarf under your bed and say you've lost it.
b) Wear the scarf but only when you go round to her house so she can see you're wearing it.
c) Thank her for making such an effort and wear the scarf to school every day.

FIND OUT HOW YOU SCORED!

MOSTLY As

Oh no! Sometimes you don't say the right things and you often upset your friend. Perhaps you should think first about what you're going to say to your friend and, if it's hurtful, rethink your words carefully.

MOSTLY Bs

Not bad. You are true to your friends. You always support them but give an honest opinion about things, too. You are usually there when your friend needs you, but sometimes you might slip up.

MOSTLY Cs

Congratulations! You really are a wonderful pal. Let's just hope that your friends are as nice to you as you always are to them!

Sleepover Picture Collection

Take pictures of all your friends at the sleepover. Here's some space to display them.

CREATE YOUR OWN FACE
SILHOUETTE

Why not add to your sleepover picture collection, and have fun with this game at the same time. Draw silhouettes of each of your friends and jumble up the images. Then try to guess whose silhouette each one is.

What you'll need:
- Plain paper • Blu-Tack
- Pen or pencil
- Acrylic or thick poster paint
- Paintbrushes
- A friend to help!

Close the curtains or wait until it is dark outside. Switch on a light. Then Blu-Tack some paper to a wall (ask permission first).

1

2

Stand sideways between the light and the paper on the wall so that the side of your face casts a sharp shadow outline on the paper. Don't stand too close to the wall, though.

3

Ask your friends to draw around the outline of your head. Take the paper down and paint inside the head shape.

Mix up the different silhouettes and guess who is who!

Girl Talk 2003 YEA[R]

	JANUARY	FEBRUARY	MARCH	APRIL	MAY	JUNE
MON						
TUES				1		
WED	1 New Year's Day			2		
THURS	2			3	1	
FRI	3			4	2	
SAT	4	1 Yuan Tan (Chinese New Year)	1	5	3	
SUN	5	2	2	6	4	1
MON	6	3	3	7	5 Children's Day (Japanese Festival)	2
TUES	7	4	4	8	6	3
WED	8	5	5 Al-Hijra (Muslim New Year's Day)	9	7	4
THURS	9	6	6	10	8	5
FRI	10	7	7	11	9	6
SAT	11	8	8	12	10	7
SUN	12	9	9	13	11	8
MON	13	10	10	14	12	9
TUES	14	11	11	15	13	10
WED	15	12	12	16	14	11
THURS	16	13	13	17	15	12
FRI	17	14 Valentine's Day	14	18 Good Friday	16	13
SAT	18	15	15	19	17	14
SUN	19	16	16	20 Easter Sunday	18	15
MON	20	17	17	21	19	16
TUES	21	18	18 Holi (Hindu Spring Festival)	22	20	17
WED	22	19	19	23	21	18
THURS	23	20	20	24	22	19
FRI	24	21	21	25	23	20
SAT	25	22 Girl Talk's 8th Birthday!	22	26	24	21
SUN	26	23	23	27	25	22
MON	27	24	24	28	26	23
TUES	28	25	25	29	27	24
WED	29	26	26	30	28	25
THURS	30	27	27		29	26
FRI	31	28	28		30	27
SAT			29		31	28
SUN			30			29
MON			31			30

R PLANNER

JULY

AUGUST

SEPTEMBER

OCTOBER

NOVEMBER

DECEMBER

JULY	AUGUST	SEPTEMBER	OCTOBER	NOVEMBER	DECEMBER	
		1			1	MON
1		2			2	TUES
2		3	1		3	WED
3		4	2		4	THURS
4	1	5	3		5	FRI
5	2	6	4	1	6	SAT
6	3	7	5	2	7	SUN
7	4	8	6 Yom Kippur (Day when Jews ask God's forgiveness)	3	8	MON
8	5	9	7	4	9	TUES
9	6	10	8	5 Bonfire Night	10	WED
10	7	11	9	6	11	THURS
11	8	12	10	7	12	FRI
12	9	13	11	8	13	SAT
13	10	14	12	9	14	SUN
14	11	15	13	10	15	MON
15	12	16	14	11	16	TUES
16	13	17	15	12	17	WED
17	14	18	16	13	18	THURS
18	15	19	17	14	19	FRI
19	16	20	18	15	20	SAT
20	17	21	19	16	21	SUN
21	18	22	20	17	22	MON
22	19	23	21	18	23	TUES
23	20 Janmashtimi (The birth of Lord Krishna)	24	22	19	24 Christmas Eve	WED
24	21	25	23	20	25 Christmas Day	THURS
25	22	26	24	21	26 Boxing Day	FRI
26	23	27 Rosh Hashana (Jewish New Year)	25	22	27	SAT
27	24	28	26	23	28	SUN
28	25	29	27 Ramadam begins (Muslim Festival with fasting from Dawn to Dusk)	24	29	MON
29	26	30	28	25	30	TUES
30	27		29	26	31	WED
31	28		30	27		THURS
	29		31 Halloween	28		FRI
	30			29		SAT
	31			30		SUN
						MON

ANIMAL ANTICS

Advice from our very own pet vet, Emma Milne.

WHY DOES YOUR PET DO THE THINGS IT DOES?

Our pets do lots of things that seem very strange to us. Most of these things are built into our animals and date back to the time when they lived in the wild. Here we take a look at the most common habits that puzzle us.

Why does my dog turn round in circles before he lies down?

Dogs do this because in the wild they need to make a bed. They sleep in long grass. Turning round in circles flattens the grass down and makes a nice, comfortable bed for the night.

Why does my dog bring me sticks and balls?

Dogs in the wild live in packs and that is the way your dog sees your family. You are their pack. The dogs go off hunting and bring back food and bones for the rest of the pack. Your dog brings you sticks and balls because that is his reward for you in place of food.

Why does my dog bark at people at the door?

Dogs are very territorial. This means that they see your home as the pack's area and no one else's. They feel the need to protect your family and the territory. When someone comes to the door your dog is saying, "Stay away, this is our place and we are going to keep it!"

Why does my cat pad my stomach when I stroke him?

Lots of cats make a padding motion when they are being fussed over. This is when they are most happy. It stems from when they were kittens. Kittens pad against their mum's tummies to stimulate her to give them milk. This is the most satisfying time for a kitten. The behaviour carries on into adult life and comes out when your cat is happy. This is when he is having a cuddle and plenty of fuss from you.

Why is my rabbit scared of me?

Rabbits are naturally very timid creatures. In the wild they are prey for lots of animals. This means they are always on the look out for bigger animals that might hurt them. We often forget how scary we must look to a small rabbit. Also, they live in big groups in the wild and all look out for each other. When they are on their own they are even more nervous. You need to be gentle and give them plenty of time to realize you aren't going to hurt them.

Why does my hamster chew his cage?

Hamsters' teeth keep growing throughout their entire lives. The teeth wear against each other and the things they chew. This keeps the teeth healthy, strong and the right length. Pet hamsters don't have many natural things to chew but they still feel the need to do it. You need to give them lots of nice things to chew. If they don't have anything they will use whatever there is. This is usually their cage!

Why does my budgie pull his feathers out?

Budgies and other birds live in massive flocks in the wild. They feel very secure in big numbers and are very sociable birds. They spend lots of time flying and exploring. When birds are caged, especially on their own, it is a very strange situation for them. Their favourite thing is flying and they are suddenly not able to this. They quickly become very bored. As a result of this boredom they start pulling their feathers out because they are frustrated.

Why does my cat scratch the furniture and the doors?

Lots of people think that cats scratch things to keep their claws sharp but this is not the case. This is a way that cats 'mark their territory'. They have little glands on their feet that produce their own individual smell. When they scratch against things they leave their scent on it. This warns other cats away. It doesn't seem very necessary in your house, but in the wild cats use their scent to claim an area of land.

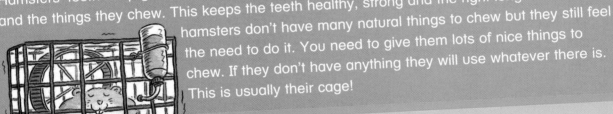

Have you ever wanted to impress your friends by drawing your own cartoon? Well, here's your chance. With this simple guide you can draw a cartoon cat and dog. Follow each drawing below, step by step, and you could animate your very own cat and dog characters.

DOG

36

Draw Cartoon Animals

CAT

What happens next? Draw the next two scenes in these boxes.

"Help! Snowy's gone," I shouted. "Help!"
I leapt out of bed and ran downstairs in my pyjamas. But even as I shouted for help, I kept thinking, "She can't have gone. She can't have gone. Snowy's always there."

I pulled back the bolts, flung open the back door and ran with bare feet across the muddy grass to her cage.

Snowy is my pet rabbit and I love her more than anything in the world. She's a Netherland Dwarf with gorgeous white fur, black eyes and the cutest little ears. She's really intelligent and I'm sure she knows her name because her ears prick up whenever I call out to her. My brother thinks I'm daft.

"Rabbits don't know their own name," he says. "They're dumb."

"Not half as dumb as you," I tell him. But I don't bother to argue. It's not worth arguing with my little brother about something as wonderful as Snowy.

Every afternoon, as soon as I get back from school, I rush out to see her in the garden. If ever I'm feeling sad and it seems that everything is going wrong, I talk to her and she understands exactly how I feel. And when I'm happy, I run out to share my excitement with her. I let her out of the hutch and she hops around sniffing the flowers and nibbling the grass. If it's raining, I bring her into the house and she hops around the kitchen and sitting room. Sometimes she even hops up the stairs, although she finds it a bit confusing getting down. So I carry her down in my arms and cuddle her until it's time to put her back in her hutch.

Every night the last thing I do is look out of my window and whisper good night

PANIC!

to her. And every morning the first thing I do is draw back the curtains and say good morning.

But not today. Now, with the rain trickling down my face, I stare at her empty hutch and a cold shiver runs down my back as I remember. Last night I heard howling outside in the garden. Startled, I woke up and peeped through the curtains. It was a clear, starlit night and the moon was full. I could see Snowy's white coat in the moonlight. So I closed my eyes and slept. Now, I realize what a fool I've been. If only I'd stayed awake longer. If only I'd got up and brought Snowy into the house.

"Snowy, where are you?" I call out to the garden. "Snowy, please come back."

Dripping and cold, I do a tour of the lawn and flowerbeds, pushing aside leaves and lifting flowers. I bend down to peer under the garden seat and I pull everything out of the tumbledown shed. No Snowy. There's a fence between our garden and the neighbour's. Can she have burrowed under there? I run all the length of it, looking for holes, and I keep praying to myself, "Please, Snowy, please be safe."

Then at the bottom of the garden by the back fence, I see something white. Something not moving. Something lying very still. My heart drops down into my feet. I step towards it, hardly able to breathe, and stop. In front of it, also not moving, also lying very still is something reddish-brown, something with

a pointed nose and pointed ears. Snowy's right ear twitches. She's alive! I want to sing and dance. But then the other creature's right ear twitches, so does its left ear and its pointed nose. The two creatures stare at each other, ears up, noses twitching. Who will make the first move? I wonder. And then I know.

Slowly, quietly, terrified that I might scare Snowy away, even more terrified that the fox might pounce, I tip-toe forwards. I don't feel the rain or the cold any more. I don't feel anything other than determination to hold Snowy in my arms again. Without knowing when or how I made the decision, I jump forwards with arms outstretched. Within seconds a wriggling, wet, soft and cuddly creature is in my arms. The fox cub looks up at me, its large brown eyes surprised and hurt. For a moment we stare at each other, then it turns and disappears into the undergrowth.

Perhaps he wanted to be friends with Snowy? Perhaps he wanted to have someone to play with in the wild overgrown garden? I'll never know. I hold Snowy tightly against me, whispering her name, telling her how much I love her. Her ears twitch in recognition, and it's difficult to say whose heart is beating faster.

THE END

39

ANIMAL PUZZLES

Animal Magic

How many animals can you find hidden in the letter chain?

OLMOUSEBCATORTOISEEDOGIRAFFEELEPHANTONCOWEVRABBITSHEEPE

Mouse, Cat, Tortoise, Dog, Giraffe, Elephant, Cow, Rabbit, Sheep

ANIMAL WORD WHEEL

Here are six animal names that all have one missing letter in common. Can you unscramble the letters and then find out what the missing letter is?

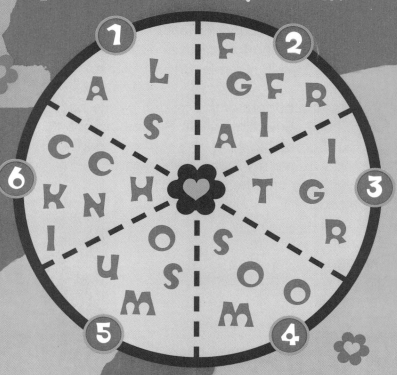

TRAVEL GAMES

You need at least two people to play these games — but you can play them wherever you go!

Take it in turns to come up with answers following one of these two suggestions. The first person to run out of ideas loses.

1 Name as many types of dog as you can.

2 Name as many animals with a tail as you can.

A DIFFERENT BREED

See if you can find these dog names in the word search below.

ALSATIAN
SPANIEL
LABRADOR
POODLE
RED SETTER
DALMATIAN
BULLDOG
GREYHOUND
DOBERMAN
TERRIER
AFGHAN HOUND
CORGI
BOXER
JACK RUSSELL
ST BERNARD
COLLIE

```
D O M J N V N A M R E B O D Z
S D L G A U A R T V E R L E S
I B N A L C E R Y Y L E H J W
F M U U B X K I A S D T L S A
X H W L O R Z R M K O T S B L
T I D B L H A U U G O E D I S
Y L M L V D N D R S P S Q T A
V G F E B A O A O Y S D R T T
S E I L L O C G H R P E O W I
P Z A T I X W U V G M R L C A
A D R A N R E B T S F E E L N
N D N U O H Y E R G F A J B Q
I N A I T A M L A D N J K B O
E I G R O C W E X R S J Z Y J
L R E I R R E T K D Y K W O O
```

ODD ONE OUT!

Which of these pets is a vegetarian?

1 Dog
2 Cat
3 Snake
4 Goldfish
5 Rabbit

Answer: Rabbit

WORD WIZARD

See how many new words you can make from just these letters.

RABBIT HUTCH

We found a huge 92. How many can you find?

41

WHAT TYPE OF TV STAR ARE YOU?

DO OUR QUIZ AND ADD UP YOUR SCORE AND SEE!

1 What would you like to be famous for?
a) Helping to save the planet from global warming.
b) Winning lots of Oscars.
c) Hosting the best TV show ever.
d) Discovering the Loch Ness Monster.

2 You see a big spider in the bath. What do you do?
a) Run screaming out of the bathroom.
b) Leave it where it is because it's perfectly happy and so are you.
c) Grab whoever's in the house and tell them to dispose of it.
d) Catch the spider in a glass and let it free in the garden.

3 Your friend asks you to help her bake a birthday cake for her sister. Do you:
a) Suggest making a super-healthy cake that her pets can eat as well.
b) You don't really want to get your hands dirty, so you say you'll read a recipe out to her and she can do the baking.
c) Roll your sleeves up, wash your hands and get stuck in.
d) Suggest that you have a baking party, then everyone can join in the hard work. Plus, it'll be a perfect opportunity for you to show off your baking skills.

Are you a drama queen?

4 You are asked to help with the school play. What would you like to do best?
a) Perform in the starring role.
b) Train an animal to appear.
c) Warm up the audience with jokes before the play.
d) Point out seats to the arriving guests.

Have

5 You have been asked to organize a surprise birthday party for your best friend. Do you:
a) Immediately start planning. Make a list of who to invite and what party food to have.
b) Organize an animal-themed surprise party with snake sweets and plastic spiders.
c) Ask all the guests to turn up in fancy dress as their favourite TV star.
d) Decide to provide the entertainment at the party with a few jokes of your own.

Would you be a magic meteorologist?

7 You and your friends get caught outside in a shower of rain. Do you:
a) Dance and sing.
b) Take shelter and say, "It will soon stop."
c) Curse and wail.
d) Stride on, smiling bravely.

8 You win a holiday in a TV competition. Which one would you choose?
a) Africa, to go on safari.
b) Hollywood, to see a film being made.
c) Iceland, to see icebergs and hot geysers.
d) A theme park, for lots of exciting rides and fairground stalls.

Does nature come naturally to you?

6 You are given some money to buy some clothes. Would you choose:
a) A smart trouser suit.
b) A glittery party dress.
c) A pair of jeans and some cool trainers.
d) A striking zebra-striped top and miniskirt.

How did you score?

	1	2	3	4	5	6	7	8
A	4	1	3	2	2	1	3	2
B	2	3	1	1	4	4	1	3
C	1	4	2	4	3	2	2	1
D	3	2	4	3	3	1	3	4

Up to 14:
You are a born actor. You would make a good star. Audition for a dramatic part in a TV soap opera or even a feature film. Who knows, you could even be in a Hollywood movie!

Between 14 and 18:
You are practical and good at explaining things. You always look on the bright side of things. You should read the weather.

Between 22 and 25:
You are a brave adventurer who loves animals – a perfect natural history presenter! You would feel at home in the depths of a jungle or on safari. As long as there are animals around, you're happy!

Between 33 and 36:
You're so confident in front of an audience. You'd make a great game show host. Why not try out some of your own jokes and questions on your friends and family for practice?

t the pzazz for presenting?

The Write Stuff!

Ever wanted to put words into the mouths of your favourite soap stars? Have a go!

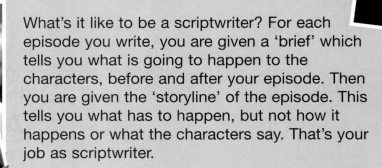

With three, four or even five episodes each week, every TV soap opera needs a whole team of scriptwriters to write all those words.

What's it like to be a scriptwriter? For each episode you write, you are given a 'brief' which tells you what is going to happen to the characters, before and after your episode. Then you are given the 'storyline' of the episode. This tells you what has to happen, but not how it happens or what the characters say. That's your job as scriptwriter.

First you have to organize the storyline, scene by scene, deciding where each bit of the story (the 'action') will take place (the 'location') and at what time of day. Once this has been approved by the script editor, you are ready to start putting words into the mouths of the characters. This is called writing 'dialogue'. The pages of dialogue and the descriptions of the action for every scene make up your 'script'.

Have a go at writing a script for our soap. It's called 'School Ties'. But first...

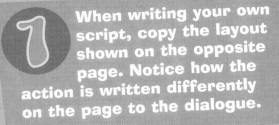

TIPS FROM THE TOP!

1 When writing your own script, copy the layout shown on the opposite page. Notice how the action is written differently on the page to the dialogue.

2 A good mix of action and dialogue will make a lively script.

3 Try to know what the ending of your story (or 'plot') will be before you begin. With the beginning and the end of your plot already worked out, you can make the action and dialogue in between as exciting as possible.

4 It really helps to write about things you know about. Even if you are writing something fantastic, the characters may still have the same thoughts and feelings as you and your friends!

5 Read your script out loud – it seems like a funny thing to do when you're sitting on your own, but it really helps!

6 ENJOY writing!

SCHOOL TIES

Read the story so far and then look at the dialogue below. See if you can finish writing the scene. How do you think it will end?

THE STORY SO FAR

Charlotte and Heather were best friends for years until Charlotte's parents decided to pay for her to go to a different school. Heather thought Charlotte's new school sounded cool because there was no school uniform. Charlotte loved her new school and told Heather thrilling stories about all the other girls there. Over time Heather had seen less and less of Charlotte. But one Friday afternoon Charlotte shows up at Heather's house looking pretty sorry for herself. Can they still be best friends?

SCENE 1.
INTERIOR. HEATHER'S BEDROOM.

HEATHER IS STILL IN HER SCHOOL UNIFORM. SHE IS SITTING AT HER DESK DOING HER HOMEWORK WHEN THERE IS A KNOCK ON THE DOOR.

HEATHER: Hello?

CHARLOTTE ENTERS.

HEATHER: I didn't hear the doorbell.

CHARLOTTE: Your mum let me in. Heather, we have to talk.

HEATHER: (GETTING CROSS) What about? Your horse-riding friends? Or the girl whose daddy owns a yacht?

CHARLOTTE: Heather! Please hear me out. It's not like you think it is. I know my school sounds better than yours, but actually it's a real drag.

HEATHER: (TUGGING OFF HER SCHOOL TIE) Wearing this stupid school tie is a drag.

CHARLOTTE: It's not like you think, Heather. Not wearing a uniform is really hard because everyone has the latest clothes and that's just like a uniform in itself. And it's really hard to concentrate on your sums when everyone's laughing at you because you haven't got the latest trainers.

HEATHER: You sound like my mum!

CHARLOTTE: Maybe your mum is right!

THEY BOTH LAUGH.

CHARLOTTE: I'm sorry I haven't seen you for a while. I got a bit behind in my schoolwork and I had some catching up to do. I know I haven't been a very good friend. I want to make up for it now. Can we go for a walk in the park and feed the squirrels, like we used to?

What do you think will happen next? Do you think Charlotte and Heather will decide to stay best friends? Maybe Heather will decide that it's time the two girls went their separate ways. Or maybe Charlotte will realize that there are good and bad things about both schools and the two girls will make a pact to share all the news and gossip from their two different schools. You decide!

MAKE IT! Fluffy Nail Varnish Box

WHAT YOU'LL NEED:
Scissors • Wet wipes box • Pink fur • PVA glue
Three pieces of pink foam • Pink material
Hair bead • Nail art stickers

STEP 1

Cut the pink fur to the right length so that it fits around the edge of the box. Use the PVA glue to stick the fur around the box.

STEP 2

Cut two pieces of foam to size and stick one on top of the lid and the other inside the lid. Then use the pink material to line the inside of the box, remembering to save a little piece for later.

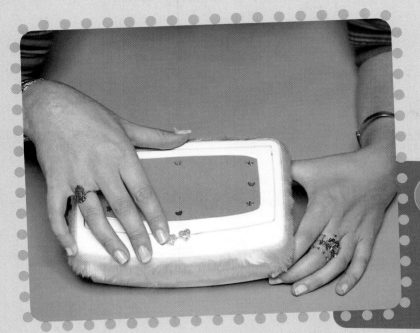

Open up the hair bead and stick it on to the presser that opens the box. Then decorate the lid with the nail stickers.

STEP 4

Cut out a flower shape from the last piece of foam. Then cut out a centre for the flower from the left-over material from Step 2. Stick the flower on the top of the box.

Your box is now ready!

Have tons of fun filling it with all your favourite nail varnishes!

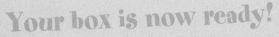

Fashion Past and

Spring, summer, autumn, winter – fashion changes with the seasons, as any dedicated follower of fashion knows. As we rush to the shops to get the latest look, we are following in a long line of fashion fiends.

Visit dazzling displays of costume around the country. We've listed some of the largest collections here (check opening times using the telephone numbers or websites). But don't forget your local museum – many have displays of costume, too.

Old and New at the V&A

For the dedicated fashion watcher, the Dress Collection at the V&A Museum in South Kensington, London, is a must. Starting from 1705, the display moves through to the present day.

If it's the fashions of today that you are interested in, then visit the V&A website, **www.vam.ac.uk**, to find out about Fashion in Motion held four times a year – designer clothes on real models who walk through the museum. You can also phone the museum for more information on **020 7942 2000**.

You can also see costumes in the New British Galleries – Margaret Laton's jacket, c. 1620. © V&A Museum.

George IV and Brighton Style

Recently re-opened in the Brighton Museum & Art Gallery, you will find a gallery of Fashion and Style that includes royal fashions in the time of George IV contrasting with clothes worn by twentieth-century rebels – mods and rockers, punks and skinheads. You may even be able to try on reproduction clothing and discover just what it was like to wear the fashions of the past. Find out more at **www.brighton-hove.gov.uk/bhc/museums/brighton** or call **01273 290000**.

Herald woman's Attendant's outfit worn at George IV's coronation, 1821. Brighton Museum & Art Gallery.

Scottish Style

If you are in Scotland, then visit the Shambellie House Museum of Costume near Dumfries to see fashions worn in Victorian and Edwardian times. You can find out more by visiting the website at **www.nms.ac.uk/costume** or calling **01387 850375**.

Phone numbers and website addresses correct at time of going to press.

46

Present

Shoe Heaven

If you are mad about shoes, then visit the footwear collection at the Central Museum & Art Gallery in Northampton. Followers of Fashion is an exciting new gallery with a display of shoes from 1660 to the present day. Discover just how high a heel can be in No Pain No Gain, or view shoes designed for tripping across the dance floor in Dancing Queen. Visit their website at **www.northampton.gov.uk/Museums/default.htm** for more information or call **01604 238548**.

Platforms and party shoes. Reproduced by permision of Northampton Museums & Art Gallery.

Decoration and Lace

Nottingham is famed as a centre of lace making and you can see lots of examples of this beautiful and fascinating craft in the Museum of Costume and Textiles, Castlegate, Nottingham. There are some stunning dresses from the eighteenth and nineteenth centuries as well as some more modern clothes. Call **0115 915 3500** for more information or visit their website at **www.nottinghamcity.gov.uk**.

Printed rayon dress, 1969-70. Museum of Costume & Textiles, Nottingham.

Minis in Manchester

The Gallery of Costume at Platt Hall in Manchester is always worth a visit – it has themed displays that change constantly. In 2003 you can see some beautiful 17th-century dresses covered in the most exquisite embroidery. You can also see a display of fashion from the 1960s to 1990s - Quant to Westwood: Fashion since the Sixties. Contact the gallery on **0161 224 5217** or visit their website at **www.cityartgalleries.org.uk**.

A Touch of Ireland

Springhill is an atmospheric 17th-century house in Co. Londonderry, Northern Ireland. An unusual and colourful costume collection exhibition with some fine 17th-century Irish pieces is housed in the old laundry building. The changing exhibition also includes 18th-century garments and flimsy evening dresses from the 1920s and 1930s. Call **028 8674 8210** for more information or visit the National Trust website **www.nationaltrust.org.uk**.

Fashionable Bath

If you're in Bath, then a visit to the Museum of Costume in the Assembly Rooms is a must. Costumes are displayed in period settings and include treasured garments from as early as the 1590s. You can contact the gallery on **01225 477789** or visit the website **www.museumofcostume.co.uk**.

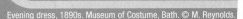
Evening dress, 1890s. Museum of Costume, Bath. © M. Reynolds.

Hi Jasmine

I miss you so much. I still can't believe you're almost on the other side of the world now. It's been 42 days since you moved to Miami and I've felt lonely every single day. It's cool that we're still best friends though. Otherwise who would I gossip with and tell all of my secrets?

A really weird thing happened at school today. Tracey – you know, the girl in the class next door who brought in her cute grey cat to the school pet day – well, she ran out of this morning's assembly, crying. Mrs Green went after her. I wonder what all that's about.

Oh yes, I went shopping on Saturday and saw a beautiful green tube top. I might ask Mum to buy it for me.

Hi there, Rosie. I've just been helping Mum with the shopping. The supermarkets are just so big over here that I was afraid I'd get lost!

I haven't made any friends yet. Well, I've sort of said hello to the girl next door, but I don't think she quite understood what I was saying because of my British accent. The people at school aren't that friendly either. Oh, I miss home. I want to be back in England, going to school with you.

I wonder what's wrong with Tracey. Perhaps you should try to find out.

I feel so lonely without you. It's not the same walking to school on my own. There's no one to play 'don't step on the paving crack' with!

I saw Tracey looking really miserable in the playground today, so I took your advice and went over to find out what the matter was. She said that she was really upset because her cat had gone missing. She's looked everywhere for it, but can't find it. How sad is that? I've invited her round to my house tomorrow after school. We will design a 'lost' poster to stick up around town in case someone has seen the cat.

Oh, I nearly forgot to tell you. I persuaded Mum to buy me that green tube top. I might wear it to the school disco.

Jessica has asked me to go to the pictures. Some of her friends will be coming too. I'm so excited. I'll have to wear that really cool pink nail varnish you sent me. I'm a bit nervous about what her friends will think of me. Mum says I have to be back home by teatime. What a bore, but I don't mind.

That's such a good idea to do 'lost' posters for Tracey's cat. You should put some of them up in the supermarket and at school. I'm going to go and try to decide what to wear for my trip to the cinema.

A story by Ruby Mather

I've just been out playing volleyball on the beach with the girl from next door I told you about. She's teaching me how to drop volleys. I used to hate doing sports when I was in England, but now, over here in the beautiful sunshine, I don't mind it at all. I guess it's 'cause Jessica is such a good coach. I'll try to e-mail you a picture of her. Anyway, I'd better go. Mum says I shouldn't use the computer for too long. See you.

I'd love to see a picture of Jessica.

Well, Tracey and I have put all the posters up around town. It was such hard work. We were exhausted. Her mum took us for a pizza afterwards to reward us for all the hard work we'd done. I hope we do find the cat.

It's been 42 days since you moved to Miami...

I'm glad you've started to make some friends in the US. Make sure you don't forget about me!

I've got some good news. WE FOUND TRACEY'S CAT! A neighbour from down the road saw one of our posters at the supermarket and recognized the cat hanging around her garden. Tracey is over the moon. She's coming over to my house tomorrow after school so we can get ready for the school disco together. She's going to borrow my green tube top. We might even have a great nail painting session like you and I used to do. Promise I'll tell you all about the disco. Keep in touch.
Love you.

No news about the cat yet. I wish you were here to help us look. Tracey is actually a really good laugh. We went to put posters up in the supermarket and ended up buying lots of chocolate ice cream to cheer ourselves up. We came back to my house and ate the whole lot. I felt quite sick!

How did your trip to the cinema go?

The trip went really well. Jessica's friends were very nice. They liked my pink nail varnish. The film was great. It won't be out in England for about three months. That's one of the advantages of living here. We all went for a milkshake after the film. Jessica's friend's thought my accent was a bit weird, but then I still think the American accent is funny. We're all going to go and hang out at the mall on Friday. Any luck with the cat hunt?

The End

51

What Do Your Clothes Say About You?

blue =
DREAMER!

red =
FUNKY!

To be a Funky Girl and customize a red vest top you will need:

- A piece of denim
- A black pen
- Scissors
- A sequin
- A needle and some thread
- One red vest top
- Glue

1 Draw a small, medium and large flower shape onto some denim fabric.

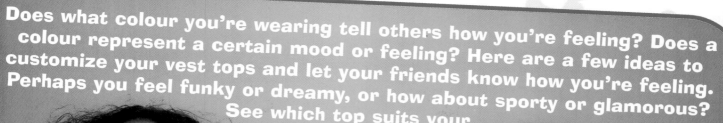

Does what colour you're wearing tell others how you're feeling? Does a colour represent a certain mood or feeling? Here are a few ideas to customize your vest tops and let your friends know how you're feeling. Perhaps you feel funky or dreamy, or how about sporty or glamorous? See which top suits your mood the best!

pink = GLAM!

white = SPORTY!

2 Cut out the three shapes and sew them together with the sequin in the centre.

3 Sew or glue the flower to one of the vest top straps.

4 Cut out and tie on some long pieces of denim to the other strap.

Why don't you make some of the other decorated vest tops shown here so your wardrobe matches all your moods!

53

Is fashion your passion?

Have a go at our fab flow chart quiz and find out!

start

Is shopping one of your favourite hobbies?

Is your wardrobe bursting at the seams? — NO / YES

When you go on holiday, do you pack more clothes than you need, just in case? — NO / YES

Do you buy new accessories nearly every weekend? — YES / NO

If you're going to a party, do you like to have something new to wear? — YES / NO

Do you look through your mum's mags for fashion tips? — YES / NO

Do you add bits to your school uniform to make it look more trendy? — YES / NO

Do you spend ages in your room doing your hair? — NO / YES

Do you ever wear nail varnish? — YES / NO

Do people sometimes ask you where you buy your clothes? — YES / NO

Have you got more than three pairs of shoes? — YES / NO

Have you got your ears pierced? — YES / NO

Do you turn to the fashion pages in *Girl Talk* first? — YES / NO

Do you and your friends spend a lot of time talking about clothes? — YES / NO

Would you rather spend your pocket money on books and computer games than on clothes? — YES

Do you know the difference between clamdiggers and pedal pushers? — YES / NO

Is it the end of the world if a hair cut goes wrong? — YES / NO

Do you think that buying new clothes before you've outgrown the old ones is pointless? — YES

You've got more clothes than Victoria Beckham and you go shopping almost as often! There's always something new you just have to have and you don't stop thinking about it until you get it. You'd like a job in fashion when you're older but, in the meantime, remember there are other things you could be doing that don't involve a spending spree!

You like being trendy, but you're not obsessed with it. You know what suits you rather than following trends just for the sake of it and you've got all sorts of other interests in your life. Well done, you've struck the perfect balance.

You're no fashion victim! As far as you're concerned, fashion is a total waste of time and you hardly give it a second thought. You'd rather be swimming, watching a film, surfing the net – in fact anything that doesn't involve shopping or clothes. That's fine, but fashion can be fun, too.

BOXING CLEVER

❀ Square up to this chequerboard challenge ❀

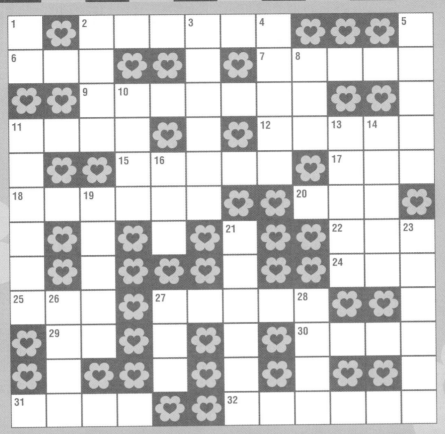

ACROSS

1 Me (1)

2 Honey, I _ _ _ _ _ _ The Kids (6)

6 Doing lots of exercise helps make you _ _ _ (3)

7 Another word for belly button (5)

9 You can go to the party if you are _ _ _ _ _ _ _ (7)

11 Aaliyah sang _ _ _ _ Than a Woman (4)

12 A stamp is frilly around the _ _ _ _ _ (5)

15 What a witch casts (5)

17 An elephant _ _ _ four knees (3)

18 Sprinkle _ _ _ _ _ _ cheese on toast – it's scrummy (6)

20 Faster than walking but slower than running (3)

22 To be crafty or sneaky about something (3)

24 What a golfer places his ball on (3)

25 December 24 is Christmas _ _ _ (3)

27 A bull let loose in a china shop might cause this (5)

29 To be _ _ not to be (2)

30 Truly bad (4)

31 If you _ _ _ _ someone something, remember to get it back (4)

32 A weeping _ _ _ _ _ _ is a beautiful tree (6)

DOWN

1 _ _ you're good, you may get a present (2)

2 To mix with a spoon (4)

3 David Beckham plays for Manchester _ _ _ _ _ _ (6)

4 People get down on their knees to do this (5)

5 Alice Through The Looking _ _ _ _ _ by Lewis Carroll (5)

8 To _ _ _ and subtract is basic arithmetic (3)

10 What a bird lives in (4)

11 Seeing one of these birds on its own is said to be bad luck (6)

13 They say this lives in a haunted house (5)

14 A bird of prey (5)

16 Something you write with (3)

19 In fairy tales, people always live happily ever _ _ _ _ _ (5)

21 In the sun our body casts a _ _ _ _ _ _ (6)

23 The colour of corn on the cob (6)

26 A small rodent, like a mouse (4)

27 A _ _ _ of beans (3)

28 You could have a car boot sale to _ _ _ _ all your old toys (4)

Winter Warmers

Try these great recipes to warm you up during the cold winter months – and impress your friends with your cooking skills. Make sure you ask an adult to help you.

Sizzling Sauces

Barbecue Gravy

Makes 150 ml (1/4 pint)

INGREDIENTS

- One teaspoon of tomato paste
- Two tablespoons of red wine vinegar
- Two tablespoons of brown sugar
- Two tablespoons of Worcestershire sauce
- 150 ml (1/4 pint) water

1 Stir all the ingredients in a saucepan over a low heat until everything has blended together.

2 Bring to boil and let the gravy bubble gently for 10 minutes.

Hot Honey Sauce

Makes 150 ml (1/4 pint)

INGREDIENTS

- 110 ml (4 fl oz) water
- Two teaspoons of cornflour
- Two teaspoons of lemon juice
- Two teaspoons of soy sauce
- Four teaspoons of tomato ketchup
- Two tablespoons of honey

1 Mix all the ingredients in a cup, except for the honey.

2 Put the honey in a saucepan and heat it gently until it starts to bubble. Mix in the other ingredients and let the mixture bubble for a minute.

Serve tasty barbecue-flavour gravy with a meaty meal instead of ordinary gravy. Serve the hot honey sauce with beefburgers, pork chops or on cooked rice.

A marinade is a tasty liquid that you normally soak meat in overnight in the fridge. These marinades could also be used to marinate vegetables. Try making delicious kebabs with cubes of courgettes, peppers, parsnips or onions. Cut the vegetables to about the same size and boil them for a minute or two before marinating. Leave the kebabs in the marinade for about 30 minutes and then grill for about 10 minutes. The taste of the marinade comes out when the meat or vegetables are cooked.

Teriyake Marinade

INGREDIENTS

- 110 ml (4 fl oz) soy sauce
- 75 g (3 oz) clear honey
- One clove of crushed garlic (ask an adult to do this) or a teaspoon of ready-prepared garlic
- 1/2 teaspoon of ground ginger

Serve chilli with plain rice. Or, if you prefer, leave it out altogether.

INGREDIENTS

- 450 g (1 lb) beef, lamb or vegetarian quorn mince
- One onion
- 50 g (2 oz) tomato paste
- One big can of baked beans
- One teaspoon of chilli powder
- Two tablespoons of milk
- Pepper and salt
- One dessertspoon of brown sugar

1 Brown the mince in a frying pan. Stir it round with a wooden spatula until it is brown all over.

2 Put the mince in a big saucepan and add the other ingredients. Stir them round and let them cook gently until the meat is tender (about an hour).

Marinade Heaven

Lemon Herb Marinade

INGREDIENTS

- 110 ml (4 fl oz) olive oil
- 55 ml (2 fl oz) lemon juice
- 55 ml (2 fl oz) white wine vinegar
- Two teaspoons of freshly chopped parsley
- Two teaspoons of fresh chives snipped with scissors into little pieces
- Grated rind of a lemon
- One tablespoon of freshly chopped rosemary or one teaspoon dried rosemary

Follow the instructions below for how to make the marinade recipes.

1 Mix everything in a bowl and pour it over some meat/vegetables in a shallow glass dish. Make sure the meat/vegetables are covered.

2 Leave the meat/vegetables to marinate for a few hours in the fridge (preferably overnight) before the meat/vegetables are cooked.

Continued over page

THE END

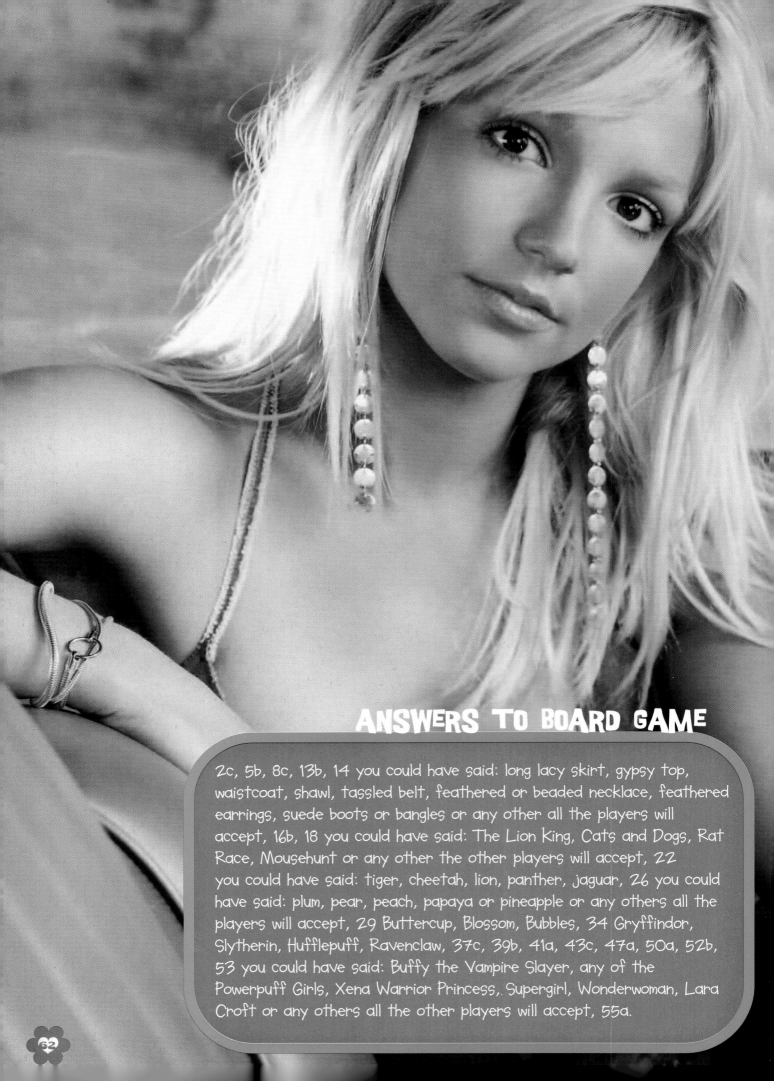

ANSWERS TO BOARD GAME

2c, 5b, 8c, 13b, 14 you could have said: long lacy skirt, gypsy top, waistcoat, shawl, tassled belt, feathered or beaded necklace, feathered earrings, suede boots or bangles or any other all the players will accept, 16b, 18 you could have said: The Lion King, Cats and Dogs, Rat Race, Mousehunt or any other the other players will accept, 22 you could have said: tiger, cheetah, lion, panther, jaguar, 26 you could have said: plum, pear, peach, papaya or pineapple or any others all the players will accept, 29 Buttercup, Blossom, Bubbles, 34 Gryffindor, Slytherin, Hufflepuff, Ravenclaw, 37c, 39b, 41a, 43c, 47a, 50a, 52b, 53 you could have said: Buffy the Vampire Slayer, any of the Powerpuff Girls, Xena Warrior Princess, Supergirl, Wonderwoman, Lara Croft or any others all the other players will accept, 55a.